Intercessory Prayer Journal

R.K. McWilliams

ISBN: 978-0-9850029-6-1

Published by Gold Writer Publishing

Rosemary (R.K.) McWilliams

Email: rkmcwilliamsbooks@gmail.com

rkmcwilliams.blogspot.com

Table of Contents

DEDICATION

To my husband, my covenant prayer partner.
To my father, a praying man.
To my mother, a praying woman.
To my Aunt Susie Sorci, an intercessor,
whose prayers were key
in leading her entire family to Christ.
And most of all, to God, my Father,
who sat with me, teaching me to pray.

Introduction

"But without faith it is impossible to please Him, for he who comes to God must believe that He is, and that He is a rewarder of those who diligently seek Him."
Hebrews 11:6

I enter my prayer room, close the door behind me, and sit in my "prayer chair"—an old 1940s-style rocker, handed down to me from my father. My hands cup over the wooden arms and I remember that my father loved this old rocker and probably said many-a-prayer sitting in it. It's re-upholstered now but still holds great sentiment. As I slowly rock back and forth, I continue the prayer journey.

I turn on soft worship music, close my eyes and quiet my mind. I whisper Psalm 51:10-11. "Create in me a clean heart, O God, and renew a steadfast spirit within me. Do not cast me away from Your presence, and do not take Your Holy Spirit from me." After a few minutes, when my heart is still, I reach for my Bible and *Intercessory Prayer Journal*. I enter into prayer using the Lord's Prayer (Matthew 6:9-13) as a model, as Jesus taught. Many faiths and people of prayer, such as John Wesley, learned to pray this prayer from the heart, aligning it with the Lord's heart, as follows: (Add your own words to make it personal).

Our Father in heaven, hallowed be Your name. I pray, "Lord, holy, holy, holy, is your name. You are worthy of all my praise. Yahweh, the Holy One of Israel. Wonderful, Counselor, Prince of Peace, Mighty God. You are the Way, the Truth, and the Life. Worthy is the name above all names."

Your kingdom come, Your will be done on earth as it is in heaven. "Lord, let your heavenly will be done in my life and the lives of my loved ones."

Give us this day, our daily bread. "Father, whatever I need for today, spiritually, physically, mentally, and financially, grant it, that I might be your hands, ears, and eyes here on earth to further the Kingdom of Heaven."

Forgive us our debts (sins) as we forgive our debtors. "Cleanse my heart and conscience,

Lord, as I forgive all those who have offended me and help me to live an un-offended life, which you made possible through your Son, Jesus. I forgive myself too. I know Your Word says that I must be in right relationship with others to be in right relationship with You" (Matthew 6:15).

And do not lead us into temptation, but deliver us from the evil one. "Thank you, Lord, that you protect those that are submitted to You and through the power of the cross and the blood of Jesus Christ, "sin has no dominion over me" (Romans 6:14). Thank you that "he who dwells in the secret place of the Most High shall abide under the shadow of the Almighty" (Psalm 91:1).

For Yours is the kingdom and the power and the glory forever. Amen. "There is no other god but You. Your kingdom is one of power, authority, and glory. I worship You alone and declare you are the Lord of my life.

I open my *Intercessory Prayer Journal*, and flip to Section 1, *Salvation Supplications*. The list seems long as I begin praying over the names of those who need salvation through Christ. Yet, remember the goodness of the Lord when He removed the blindness from the eyes of my eart and I became "born again" (John 3:5). I could suddenly see my sin and my need for a oly God to wash me clean. What incredible joy it brought, to know that Jesus made it ossible to not only change me into a new creature in Christ (2 Corinthians 5:17), but now my ssurance of heaven is given through the Holy Spirit of the living God, "by whom you were ealed for the day of redemption" (Ephesians 4:30).

earnestly pray through the list of names that they too, will find the Lord Jesus Christ as their ersonal savior and with it, eternal life in heaven through the saving power of the cross. Today, I add yet another name, dating it with today's date. I look in faith toward the day that I will be able to fill in "Date Answered" behind each and every name, knowing that the Bible says, "he who wins souls is wise" (Proverbs 11:30). I can't imagine one of them spending eternity in the torment of hell, and as long as I have breath, I will call out their names to heaven. I realize I have been given a great gift—my salvation—and now it is my responsibility to pray for others because it is the Father's heart that no man perish. "…God our Savior, who desires all men to be saved and to come to the knowledge of the truth" (1 Timothy 2:3,4).

As I continue praying, I let the Holy Spirit lead me and don't always go to each section, or follow any pattern. But, today, I have a recent photo of a loved one to add to the *Photos* section. Her picture joins the others already taped to the pages. My heart is moved to see the faces of family, friends, orphans, and ministries that I love and to let the Holy Spirit guide me into deep prayer for their needs (Romans 8:26).

I move to the next section labeled *Interceding for Others*. There's a long list of requests, but my heart warms to see how many the Lord has already answered. Yes, He is faithful and hears my prayers. I immerse myself into the requests—for healings, deliverances from addictions and bondages, and depression. Some people need finances to feed their children, some want to know You better, some are in abusive situations, and some have fears about the future. Yet, I pray in faith because "the effective, fervent prayer of a righteous man avails much" (James 5:16). I know this means that my "energetic, active" prayer is powerful and effective.

My ipod is playing, "Holy, Holy, Holy, Lord God Almighty." I stop, close my eyes and join in. "In His presence is fullness of joy," (Psalm 16:11) and there is nothing on this earth that compares to the peace I feel now.

This prepares me to move on to *Prayers for My Country and Those in Authority*. I am so thankful for my country, the Constitution, and personal freedoms in the USA. My Bible says to pray and intercede for all those in authority (1 Timothy 2:1-2). The Lord wants to heal our land (2 Chronicles 7:14). I know that even in the many problems, our hope is in the Lord, the Holy One, who pours out the "spirit of grace and supplication" (Zechariah 12:10) on those who will seek Him.

I accept the assignment as an intercessor (a mediator, or one who stands in the gap for others) to pray for His mercy and truth to be known, and for another spiritual awakening in this country. I pray for the children and future generations to know the Truth. I place my hands on the photos of my niece's two young children and pray for their futures. I earnestly pray for this country that I love, that God would rain down righteousness from heaven (Isaiah 45:8).

I cry to the Lord for Godly authority in this country so "we may lead a quiet and peaceable life in all godliness and reverence" (1 Timothy 2:2). I pray for all those in authority over me, because Romans 13 tells me that they are given for my safety. I pray for my husband, pastors, elders, deacons, lawmakers, judges, city and county officials, along with state and federal authorities. I pray for the police, sheriffs, national guard and other peacekeepers who deal daily with an increasingly volatile society. I remember their wives and children, who may fear their husbands and fathers may not come back home.

I move on to the next sections, which are mainly for my own spiritual growth: *Personal Prayers*, *Meditation on the Word*, *He Speaks to Me*, *Prophetic Words*, and *Memory Verses*. As I look at my *Personal Prayer* list, I feel so grateful for all He has done in my life. The ore time I spend in my "prayer chair" praying and meditating on the Scriptures, He changes e into a new creature in Christ, as He promised (2 Corinthians 5:17).

loving on to *Meditation on the Word,* I choose a Scripture for today—Proverbs 23. I write it my Journal and even though I have read this scripture many times before, suddenly I see omething new! The Holy Spirit drops revelation into my spirit, revealing wisdom and nderstanding that I can use for my next teaching. Perfect timing. The Word is a lamp unto y feet and a light unto my path. His wisdom brings success.

As I move to Section 7, *He Speaks To Me Daily Journal,* I take a second to make sure there are no hindrances to hearing God's voice, such as unconfessed sin, deliberate rebellion, disobedience, or choosing to be busy, rather than putting the Lord first and developing a prayer time with Him. I think about Isaiah 59:2 which says "But your iniquities have separated you from your God; and your sins have hidden His face from you, so that He will not hear." I confess, repent (change my mind) and once again, feel the peace. 1 John 1:9 says,

"If we confess our sins, He is faithful and just to forgive us our sins and to cleanse us from all unrighteousness."

Now, I ask, "Holy Spirit, what are you saying to me today? And, more importantly, I listen to Him. He speaks in several ways:

1. Through a still, small voice. 1 Kings 19:11-12
2. Through the Scriptures. Romans 10:17
3. Through open and closed doors. Revelation 3:7
4. By letting peace rule your heart. Colossians 3:15
5. Through other people, especially authority. John 2:1-11, Romans 13:1-4

Source: *Ten Steps Toward Christ,* Jimmy Evans

"My sheep hear My voice, and I know them, and they follow Me" (John 10:27). Today, I take a minute to flip back and re-read things the Lord revealed to me in previous months. I am encouraged that I, as a child of God, can hear His voice.

Next, I turn to Section 8, *Prophetic Words*. I read over some personal prophetic words that I received from ministers and pastors with proven, righteous ministries. A timely prophetic word gives guidance and direction, with edification, exhortation, and comfort (1 Corinthians 14:3). Today, I pray it, declare it, and, as my faith builds, I expect it to happen. Job 22:28 NKJV says, "You will also declare a thing, and it will be established for you; so light will shine on your ways." My prayer is, "Thank you for this word, Lord, which confirms in my heart, and I know, will produce Your will in my life. Thank You for prophetic words that wer spoken over me . . . some, many years ago . . . along with words of wisdom and knowledge (1 Corinthians 12:8), that are coming to pass right now."

I ask the Lord to bless other credible prophetic leaders, who regularly hear what God is saying to the body of Christ and to our nation. Amos 3:2 says, "Surely the Lord God does nothing, unless He reveals His secret to His servants the prophets." I take time to pray over these words that line up with the Word of God, since they reflect the heart and desires of God over certain situations.

A Final Note

Spending time in your "prayer chair" will change your life. Each day may be different in your approach, just be flexible and obey His leading. Giving Him your time will always lead to success because you will discover a deeper intimacy with the Lord. He delights in you and to hear your prayers that rise to His ears. "And your Father, who sees in secret, will reward you openly" (Matthew 6:6). It is one of the many promises He has given in His Word and it is for you today. Too many don't take the time to seek Him until they really need Him, but He wants a continuous, ongoing relationship like He had with Adam and Eve before the fall. "The Lord knows those who are His" (2 Timothy 2:19). Jesus has made it possible for us to have that kind of relationship because he took the sin we were born into, upon Himself, breaking down the wall of separation between God and man.

Finally, take time to memorize Bible verses which help you grow into a prayer warrior who stands in the gap between heaven and hell for others' sake. You will become strong, stable d fixed, under the shadow of the Almighty. You will say of the Lord, "He is my refuge and y strength, my God, in Him I will trust" (Psalm 91). And, on those days you don't know hat to pray, pray the Scriptures because . . . ***Praying the Word of God will cause you to be 00% right, 100% of the time!***

lay the Lord bless you on your prayer journey that takes you into the presence of the King.

R.K. McWilliams

"…And take the helmet of salvation,
and the sword of the Spirit, which is the word of God;
praying always with all prayer and supplication in the Spirit,
being watchful to this end with all perseverance
and supplication for all the saints…"
Ephesians 6:17-18

1

Salvation Supplications

The Biblical Road to Salvation

"Jesus answered and said to him, 'Most assuredly, I say to you, unless one is born again, he cannot see the kingdom of God'" (John 3:3). What does born again mean? In the Greek, ***born*** means **born**. However, ***again*** means **from above, from a higher place** (Strongs G509). In order to see heaven we must be born twice—once in the flesh, and once in the Spirit. "Flesh gives birth to flesh and the Spirit gives birth to spirit (John 3:6 NIV). We are not just bodies (flesh), but are spirits as well. It is our spirit that lives forever after our body dies. So, how is one born again? Please read on, then pray the Salvation Prayer below.

God has a deep love for you.

"For God so loved the world that He gave His only begotten Son, that whosoever believes in Him should not perish but have everlasting life." John 3:16

Man was born into sin.

"For all have sinned and come short of the glory of God." Romans 3:23

Sin has a penalty.

"For the wages of sin is death, but the gift of God is eternal life in Christ Jesus our Lord." Romans 6:23

Christ paid the penalty for us.

"But God demonstrated His own love toward us in that while we were still sinners, Christ died for us." Romans 5:8

Salvation is a free gift.

"For by grace are you saved through faith; and that not of yourselves: it is the gift of God: not of works, lest any man should boast." Ephesians 2:8-9

Jesus Christ is at your heart's door.

"Behold I stand at the door and knock: if any man hear My voice, and open the door, I will come in to him." Revelation 3:20

We must receive Him.

"Jesus said to him, I am the way, the truth, and the life. No one comes to the Father except through Me." John 14:6

"...that if you confess with your mouth the Lord Jesus and believe in your heart that God has raised Him from the dead, you will be saved. For with the heart one believes to righteousness and with the mouth confession is made to salvation." Romans 10:9

"But as many as received Him, to them gave He power to become the sons of God, even to them that believe on His name." John 1:12

He lives within you.

"As God has said: I will dwell in them and walk among them. I will be a Father to you and you shall be My sos and daughters, says the Lord Almighty." 2 Corinthians 6:16, 18

Salvation Prayer

Lord, I am a sinner in need of a Savior. I believe that Jesus Christ died for my sins, paying the penalty for me. I confess the Lord Jesus with my mouth and believe in my heart that God has raised Him from the dead. Wash me clean from my sins. Fill me with the Holy Spirit. I turn to You and make You Lord of my life. Help me to live for You and obey Your Word. Thank you for loving me and saving me. In Jesus name I pray. Amen

Salvation Supplications

Jesus answered and said to him, "Most assuredly, I say to you, unless one is born again, he cannot see the Kingdom of God." John 3:3

Date	Name	Date Answered

"...to open their eyes and to turn them from darkness to light, and from the power of Satan to God, that they may receive forgiveness of sins and an inheritance among those who are sanctified by faith in Me." Acts 26:18

Salvation Supplications

Jesus answered and said to him, "Most assuredly, I say to you, unless one is born again, he cannot see the Kingdom of God." John 3:3

Date	Name	Date Answered

"...to open their eyes and to turn them from darkness to light, and from the power of Satan to God, that they may receive forgiveness of sins and an inheritance among those who are sanctified by faith in Me." Acts 26:18

Salvation Supplications

Jesus answered and said to him, "Most assuredly, I say to you, unless one is born again, he cannot see the Kingdom of God." John 3:3

Date	Name	Date Answered

"...to open their eyes and to turn them from darkness to light, and from the power of Satan to God, that they may receive forgiveness of sins and an inheritance among those who are sanctified by faith in Me." Acts 26:18

Salvation Supplications

Jesus answered and said to him, "Most assuredly, I say to you, unless one is born again, he cannot see the Kingdom of God." John 3:3

Date	Name	Date Answered

"...to open their eyes and to turn them from darkness to light, and from the power of Satan to God, that they may receive forgiveness of sins and an inheritance among those who are sanctified by faith in Me." Acts 26:18

Salvation Supplications

Jesus answered and said to him, "Most assuredly, I say to you, unless one is born again, he cannot see the Kingdom of God." John 3:3

Date	Name	Date Answered

"...to open their eyes and to turn them from darkness to light, and from the power of Satan to God, that they may receive forgiveness of sins and an inheritance among those who are sanctified by faith in Me." Acts 26:18

Salvation Supplications

Jesus answered and said to him, "Most assuredly, I say to you, unless one is born again, he cannot see the Kingdom of God." John 3:3

Date	Name	Date Answered

"...to open their eyes and to turn them from darkness to light, and from the power of Satan to God, that they may receive forgiveness of sins and an inheritance among those who are sanctified by faith in Me." Acts 26:18

Salvation Supplications

Jesus answered and said to him, "Most assuredly, I say to you, unless one is born again, he cannot see the Kingdom of God." John 3:3

Date	Name	Date Answered

"...to open their eyes and to turn them from darkness to light, and from the power of Satan to God, that they may receive forgiveness of sins and an inheritance among those who are sanctified by faith in Me." Acts 26:18

Salvation Supplications

Jesus answered and said to him, "Most assuredly, I say to you, unless one is born again, he cannot see the Kingdom of God." John 3:3

Date	Name	Date Answered

"...to open their eyes and to turn them from darkness to light, and from the power of Satan to God, that they may receive forgiveness of sins and an inheritance among those who are sanctified by faith in Me." Acts 26:18

Salvation Supplications

Jesus answered and said to him, "Most assuredly, I say to you, unless one is born again, he cannot see the Kingdom of God." John 3:3

Date	Name	Date Answered

"...to open their eyes and to turn them from darkness to light, and from the power of Satan to God, that they may receive forgiveness of sins and an inheritance among those who are sanctified by faith in Me." Acts 26:18

Salvation Supplications

Jesus answered and said to him, "Most assuredly, I say to you, unless one is born again, he cannot see the Kingdom of God." John 3:3

Date	Name	Date Answered

"...to open their eyes and to turn them from darkness to light, and from the power of Satan to God, that they may receive forgiveness of sins and an inheritance among those who are sanctified by faith in Me." Acts 26:18

2

Photos

Photos

Paste photos of family, friends, orphans, and ministries that you support. Write prayers beside them.

Photos

Paste photos of family, friends, orphans, and ministries that you support. Write prayers beside them.

Photos

Paste photos of family, friends, orphans, and ministries that you support. Write prayers beside them.

Photos

Paste photos of family, friends, orphans, and ministries that you support. Write prayers beside them.

Photos

Paste photos of family, friends, orphans, and ministries that you support. Write prayers beside them.

Photos

Paste photos of family, friends, orphans, and ministries that you support. Write prayers beside them.

Photos

Paste photos of family, friends, orphans, and ministries that you support. Write prayers beside them.

3

Interceding For Others

Interceding for Others

"Bear one another's burdens, and so fulfill the law of Christ." Galatians 6:2

Date	Name	Date Answered

Interceding for Others

"Bear one another's burdens, and so fulfill the law of Christ." Galatians 6:2

Date	Name	Date Answered

Interceding for Others

"Bear one another's burdens, and so fulfill the law of Christ." Galatians 6:2

Date	Name	Date Answered

Interceding for Others

"Bear one another's burdens, and so fulfill the law of Christ." Galatians 6:2

Date	Name	Date Answered

Interceding for Others

"Bear one another's burdens, and so fulfill the law of Christ." Galatians 6:2

Date	Name	Date Answered

Interceding for Others

"Bear one another's burdens, and so fulfill the law of Christ." Galatians 6:2

Date	Name	Date Answered

Interceding for Others

"Bear one another's burdens, and so fulfill the law of Christ." Galatians 6:2

Date	Name	Date Answered

Interceding for Others

"Bear one another's burdens, and so fulfill the law of Christ." Galatians 6:2

Date	Name	Date Answered

Interceding for Others

"Bear one another's burdens, and so fulfill the law of Christ." Galatians 6:2

Date	Name	Date Answered

Interceding for Others

"Bear one another's burdens, and so fulfill the law of Christ." Galatians 6:2

Date	Name	Date Answered

Interceding for Others

"Bear one another's burdens, and so fulfill the law of Christ." Galatians 6:2

Date	Name	Date Answered

Interceding for Others

"Bear one another's burdens, and so fulfill the law of Christ." Galatians 6:2

Date	Name	Date Answered

Interceding for Others

"Bear one another's burdens, and so fulfill the law of Christ." Galatians 6:2

Date	Name	Date Answered

Interceding for Others

"Bear one another's burdens, and so fulfill the law of Christ." Galatians 6:2

Date	Name	Date Answered

Interceding for Others

"Bear one another's burdens, and so fulfill the law of Christ." Galatians 6:2

Date	Name	Date Answered

4

Prayers For My Country & Those in Authority

Prayers for My Country & Those in Authority

"If My people who are called by My name will humble themselves, and pray and seek My face, and turn from their wicked ways, then will I hear from heaven, and will forgive their sin, and will heal their land." II Chronicles 7:14

Date	Petition	Date Answered

"Therefore I exhort first of all that supplications, prayers, intercessions and giving of thanks be made for all men, for kings and all who are in authority that we may lead a quiet and peaceable life in all godliness and reverence. For this is good and acceptable in the sight of God our Savior, who desires all men to be saved and to come to the knowledge of the truth."
1 Timothy 2:1-4

Prayers for My Country & Those in Authority

"If My people who are called by My name will humble themselves, and pray and seek My face, and turn from their wicked ways, then will I hear from heaven, and will forgive their sin, and will heal their land." II Chronicles 7:14

Date	Petition	Date Answered

"Therefore I exhort first of all that supplications, prayers, intercessions and giving of thanks be made for all men, for kings and all who are in authority that we may lead a quiet and peaceable life in all godliness and reverence. For this is good and acceptable in the sight of God our Savior, who desires all men to be saved and to come to the knowledge of the truth."
1 Timothy 2:1-4

Prayers for My Country & Those in Authority

"If My people who are called by My name will humble themselves, and pray and seek My face, and turn from their wicked ways, then will I hear from heaven, and will forgive their sin, and will heal their land." II Chronicles 7:14

Date	Petition	Date Answered

"Therefore I exhort first of all that supplications, prayers, intercessions and giving of thanks be made for all men, for kings and all who are in authority that we may lead a quiet and peaceable life in all godliness and reverence. For this is good and acceptable in the sight of God our Savior, who desires all men to be saved and to come to the knowledge of the truth."
1 Timothy 2:1-4

Prayers for My Country & Those in Authority

"If My people who are called by My name will humble themselves, and pray and seek My face, and turn from their wicked ways, then will I hear from heaven, and will forgive their sin, and will heal their land." II Chronicles 7:14

Date	Petition	Date Answered

"Therefore I exhort first of all that supplications, prayers, intercessions and giving of thanks be made for all men, for kings and all who are in authority that we may lead a quiet and peaceable life in all godliness and reverence. For this is good and acceptable in the sight of God our Savior, who desires all men to be saved and to come to the knowledge of the truth."
1 Timothy 2:1-4

Prayers for My Country & Those in Authority

"If My people who are called by My name will humble themselves, and pray and seek My face, and turn from their wicked ways, then will I hear from heaven, and will forgive their sin, and will heal their land." II Chronicles 7:14

Date	Petition	Date Answered

"Therefore I exhort first of all that supplications, prayers, intercessions and giving of thanks be made for all men, for kings and all who are in authority that we may lead a quiet and peaceable life in all godliness and reverence. For this is good and acceptable in the sight of God our Savior, who desires all men to be saved and to come to the knowledge of the truth."
1 Timothy 2:1-4

Prayers for My Country & Those in Authority

"If My people who are called by My name will humble themselves, and pray and seek My face, and turn from their wicked ways, then will I hear from heaven, and will forgive their sin, and will heal their land." II Chronicles 7:14

Date	Petition	Date Answered

"Therefore I exhort first of all that supplications, prayers, intercessions and giving of thanks be made for all men, for kings and all who are in authority that we may lead a quiet and peaceable life in all godliness and reverence. For this is good and acceptable in the sight of God our Savior, who desires all men to be saved and to come to the knowledge of the truth."
1 Timothy 2:1-4

Prayers for My Country & Those in Authority

"If My people who are called by My name will humble themselves, and pray and seek My face, and turn from their wicked ways, then will I hear from heaven, and will forgive their sin, and will heal their land." II Chronicles 7:14

Date	Petition	Date Answered

"Therefore I exhort first of all that supplications, prayers, intercessions and giving of thanks be made for all men, for kings and all who are in authority that we may lead a quiet and peaceable life in all godliness and reverence. For this is good and acceptable in the sight of God our Savior, who desires all men to be saved and to come to the knowledge of the truth."
1 Timothy 2:1-4

Prayers for My Country & Those in Authority

"If My people who are called by My name will humble themselves, and pray and seek My face, and turn from their wicked ways, then will I hear from heaven, and will forgive their sin, and will heal their land." II Chronicles 7:14

Date	Petition	Date Answered

"Therefore I exhort first of all that supplications, prayers, intercessions and giving of thanks be made for all men, for kings and all who are in authority that we may lead a quiet and peaceable life in all godliness and reverence. For this is good and acceptable in the sight of God our Savior, who desires all men to be saved and to come to the knowledge of the truth."
1 Timothy 2:1-4

Prayers for My Country & Those in Authority

"If My people who are called by My name will humble themselves, and pray and seek My face, and turn from their wicked ways, then will I hear from heaven, and will forgive their sin, and will heal their land." II Chronicles 7:14

Date	Petition	Date Answered

"Therefore I exhort first of all that supplications, prayers, intercessions and giving of thanks be made for all men, for kings and all who are in authority that we may lead a quiet and peaceable life in all godliness and reverence. For this is good and acceptable in the sight of God our Savior, who desires all men to be saved and to come to the knowledge of the truth."
1 Timothy 2:1-4

Prayers for My Country & Those in Authority

"If My people who are called by My name will humble themselves, and pray and seek My face, and turn from their wicked ways, then will I hear from heaven, and will forgive their sin, and will heal their land." II Chronicles 7:14

Date	Petition	Date Answered

"Therefore I exhort first of all that supplications, prayers, intercessions and giving of thanks be made for all men, for kings and all who are in authority that we may lead a quiet and peaceable life in all godliness and reverence. For this is good and acceptable in the sight of God our Savior, who desires all men to be saved and to come to the knowledge of the truth."
1 Timothy 2:1-4

Prayers for My Country & Those in Authority

"If My people who are called by My name will humble themselves, and pray and seek My face, and turn from their wicked ways, then will I hear from heaven, and will forgive their sin, and will heal their land." II Chronicles 7:14

Date	Petition	Date Answered

"Therefore I exhort first of all that supplications, prayers, intercessions and giving of thanks be made for all men, for kings and all who are in authority that we may lead a quiet and peaceable life in all godliness and reverence. For this is good and acceptable in the sight of God our Savior, who desires all men to be saved and to come to the knowledge of the truth."
1 Timothy 2:1-4

Prayers for My Country & Those in Authority

"If My people who are called by My name will humble themselves, and pray and seek My face, and turn from their wicked ways, then will I hear from heaven, and will forgive their sin, and will heal their land." II Chronicles 7:14

Date	Petition	Date Answered

"Therefore I exhort first of all that supplications, prayers, intercessions and giving of thanks be made for all men, for kings and all who are in authority that we may lead a quiet and peaceable life in all godliness and reverence. For this is good and acceptable in the sight of God our Savior, who desires all men to be saved and to come to the knowledge of the truth."
1 Timothy 2:1-4

Prayers for My Country & Those in Authority

"If My people who are called by My name will humble themselves, and pray and seek My face, and turn from their wicked ways, then will I hear from heaven, and will forgive their sin, and will heal their land." II Chronicles 7:14

Date	Petition	Date Answered

"Therefore I exhort first of all that supplications, prayers, intercessions and giving of thanks be made for all men, for kings and all who are in authority that we may lead a quiet and peaceable life in all godliness and reverence. For this is good and acceptable in the sight of God our Savior, who desires all men to be saved and to come to the knowledge of the truth."
1 Timothy 2:1-4

Prayers for My Country & Those in Authority

"If My people who are called by My name will humble themselves, and pray and seek My face, and turn from their wicked ways, then will I hear from heaven, and will forgive their sin, and will heal their land." II Chronicles 7:14

Date	Petition	Date Answered

"Therefore I exhort first of all that supplications, prayers, intercessions and giving of thanks be made for all men, for kings and all who are in authority that we may lead a quiet and peaceable life in all godliness and reverence. For this is good and acceptable in the sight of God our Savior, who desires all men to be saved and to come to the knowledge of the truth."
1 Timothy 2:1-4

Prayers for My Country & Those in Authority

"If My people who are called by My name will humble themselves, and pray and seek My face, and turn from their wicked ways, then will I hear from heaven, and will forgive their sin, and will heal their land." II Chronicles 7:14

Date	Petition	Date Answered

"Therefore I exhort first of all that supplications, prayers, intercessions and giving of thanks be made for all men, for kings and all who are in authority that we may lead a quiet and peaceable life in all godliness and reverence. For this is good and acceptable in the sight of God our Savior, who desires all men to be saved and to come to the knowledge of the truth."
1 Timothy 2:1-4

5

Personal Prayers

JESUS

Personal Prayers

"The effective, fervent prayer of a righteous man avails much." James 5:16

Date	Request	Date Answered

Personal Prayers

"The effective, fervent prayer of a righteous man avails much." James 5:16

Date	Request	Date Answered

Personal Prayers

"The effective, fervent prayer of a righteous man avails much." James 5:16

Date	Request	Date Answered

Personal Prayers

"The effective, fervent prayer of a righteous man avails much." James 5:16

Date	Request	Date Answered

Personal Prayers

"The effective, fervent prayer of a righteous man avails much." James 5:16

Date	Request	Date Answered

Personal Prayers

"The effective, fervent prayer of a righteous man avails much." James 5:16

Date	Request	Date Answered

Personal Prayers

"The effective, fervent prayer of a righteous man avails much." James 5:16

Date	Request	Date Answered

Personal Prayers

"The effective, fervent prayer of a righteous man avails much." James 5:16

Date	Request	Date Answered

Personal Prayers

"The effective, fervent prayer of a righteous man avails much." James 5:16

Date	Request	Date Answered

Personal Prayers

"The effective, fervent prayer of a righteous man avails much." James 5:16

Date	Request	Date Answered

Personal Prayers

"The effective, fervent prayer of a righteous man avails much." James 5:16

Date	Request	Date Answered

Personal Prayers

"The effective, fervent prayer of a righteous man avails much." James 5:16

Date	Request	Date Answered

Personal Prayers

"The effective, fervent prayer of a righteous man avails much." James 5:16

Date	Request	Date Answered

Personal Prayers

"The effective, fervent prayer of a righteous man avails much." James 5:16

Date	Request	Date Answered

Personal Prayers

"The effective, fervent prayer of a righteous man avails much." James 5:16

Date	Request	Date Answered

Personal Prayers

"The effective, fervent prayer of a righteous man avails much." James 5:16

Date	Request	Date Answered

Personal Prayers

"The effective, fervent prayer of a righteous man avails much." James 5:16

Date	Request	Date Answered

6

Meditation on the Word

Meditation on the Word

"Blessed is the man who walks not in the counsel of the ungodly, nor stands in the path of sinners, nor sits in the seat of the scornful, but his delight is in the law of the Lord, and in His law he meditates day and night. He shall be like a tree planted by the rivers of water, that brings forth its fruit in its season, whose leaf also shall not wither; and whatever he does shall prosper." Psalm 1:1-3

Date: ______________________________

Scripture: ______________________________

____

____

____

____

____

Insights and Personal Application:

____

____

____

____

____

____

____

____

____

____

____

____

____

Meditation on the Word

"Blessed is the man who walks not in the counsel of the ungodly, nor stands in the path of sinners, nor sits in the seat of the scornful, but his delight is in the law of the Lord, and in His law he meditates day and night. He shall be like a tree planted by the rivers of water, that brings forth its fruit in its season, whose leaf also shall not wither; and whatever he does shall prosper." Psalm 1:1-3

Date: ______________________

Scripture: ______________________

____

____

____

____

____

Insights and Personal Application:

____

____

____

____

____

____

____

____

____

____

____

____

____

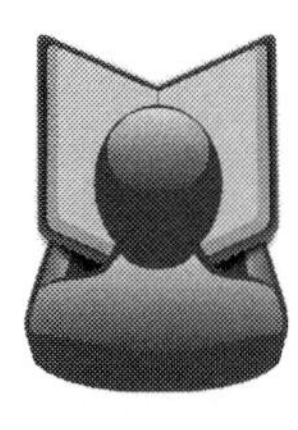

Meditation on the Word

"Blessed is the man who walks not in the counsel of the ungodly, nor stands in the path of sinners, nor sits in the seat of the scornful, but his delight is in the law of the Lord, and in His law he meditates day and night. He shall be like a tree planted by the rivers of water, that brings forth its fruit in its season, whose leaf also shall not wither; and whatever he does shall prosper." Psalm 1:1-3

Date: ______________________________

Scripture: ______________________________

____

____

____

____

____

Insights and Personal Application:

____

____

____

____

____

____

____

____

____

____

____

____

____

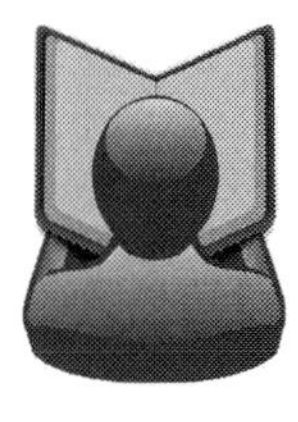

Meditation on the Word

"Blessed is the man who walks not in the counsel of the ungodly, nor stands in the path of sinners, nor sits in the seat of the scornful, but his delight is in the law of the Lord, and in His law he meditates day and night. He shall be like a tree planted by the rivers of water, that brings forth its fruit in its season, whose leaf also shall not wither; and whatever he does shall prosper." Psalm 1:1-3

Date: ______________________________

Scripture: ______________________________

____

____

____

____

____

Insights and Personal Application:

____

____

____

____

____

____

____

____

____

____

____

____

____

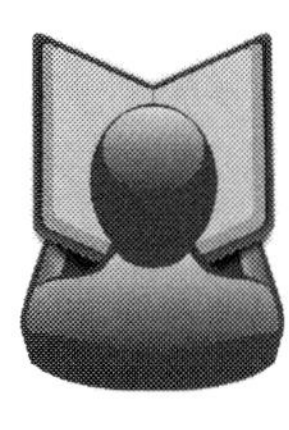

Meditation on the Word

"Blessed is the man who walks not in the counsel of the ungodly, nor stands in the path of sinners, nor sits in the seat of the scornful, but his delight is in the law of the Lord, and in His law he meditates day and night. He shall be like a tree planted by the rivers of water, that brings forth its fruit in its season, whose leaf also shall not wither; and whatever he does shall prosper." Psalm 1:1-3

Date: ______________________

Scripture: ______________________

____

____

____

____

____

Insights and Personal Application:

____

____

____

____

____

____

____

____

____

____

____

____

____

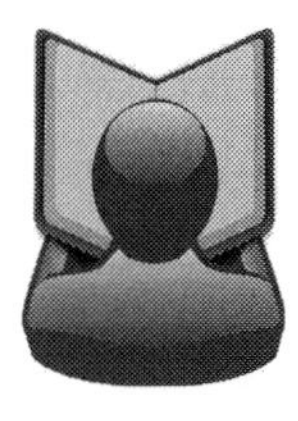

Meditation on the Word

"Blessed is the man who walks not in the counsel of the ungodly, nor stands in the path of sinners, nor sits in the seat of the scornful, but his delight is in the law of the Lord, and in His law he meditates day and night. He shall be like a tree planted by the rivers of water, that brings forth its fruit in its season, whose leaf also shall not wither; and whatever he does shall prosper." Psalm 1:1-3

Date: ______________________

Scripture: ______________________

Insights and Personal Application:

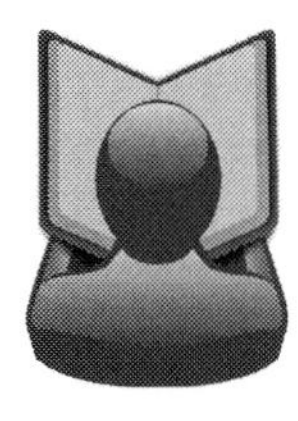

Meditation on the Word

"Blessed is the man who walks not in the counsel of the ungodly, nor stands in the path of sinners, nor sits in the seat of the scornful, but his delight is in the law of the Lord, and in His law he meditates day and night. He shall be like a tree planted by the rivers of water, that brings forth its fruit in its season, whose leaf also shall not wither; and whatever he does shall prosper." Psalm 1:1-3

Date: ______________________________

Scripture: ______________________________

____

____

____

____

____

Insights and Personal Application:

____

____

____

____

____

____

____

____

____

____

____

____

____

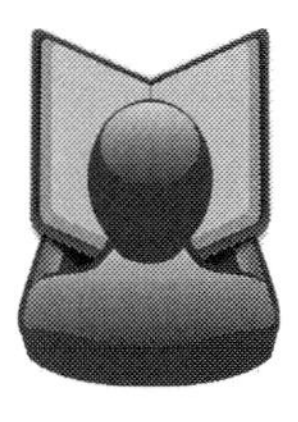

Meditation on the Word

"Blessed is the man who walks not in the counsel of the ungodly, nor stands in the path of sinners, nor sits in the seat of the scornful, but his delight is in the law of the Lord, and in His law he meditates day and night. He shall be like a tree planted by the rivers of water, that brings forth its fruit in its season, whose leaf also shall not wither; and whatever he does shall prosper." Psalm 1:1-3

Date: ______________________________

Scripture: ______________________________

____

____

____

____

____

Insights and Personal Application:

____

____

____

____

____

____

____

____

____

____

____

____

____

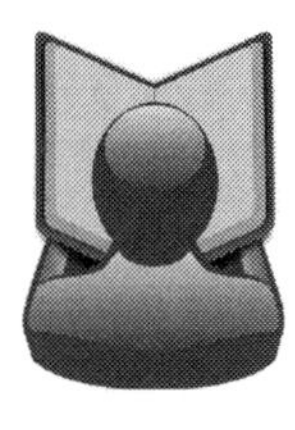

Meditation on the Word

"Blessed is the man who walks not in the counsel of the ungodly, nor stands in the path of sinners, nor sits in the seat of the scornful, but his delight is in the law of the Lord, and in His law he meditates day and night. He shall be like a tree planted by the rivers of water, that brings forth its fruit in its season, whose leaf also shall not wither; and whatever he does shall prosper." Psalm 1:1-3

Date: ______________________________

Scripture: ______________________________

____

____

____

____

____

Insights and Personal Application:

____

____

____

____

____

____

____

____

____

____

____

____

____

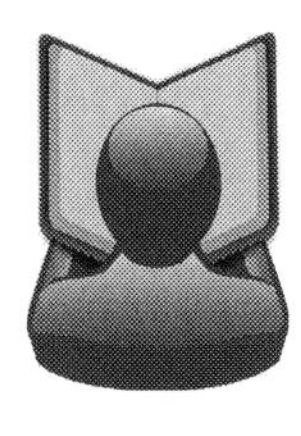

Meditation on the Word

"Blessed is the man who walks not in the counsel of the ungodly, nor stands in the path of sinners, nor sits in the seat of the scornful, but his delight is in the law of the Lord, and in His law he meditates day and night. He shall be like a tree planted by the rivers of water, that brings forth its fruit in its season, whose leaf also shall not wither; and whatever he does shall prosper." Psalm 1:1-3

Date: ______________________

Scripture: ______________________

____

____

____

____

____

Insights and Personal Application:

____

____

____

____

____

____

____

____

____

____

____

____

____

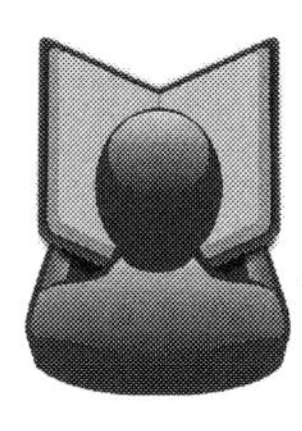

Meditation on the Word

"Blessed is the man who walks not in the counsel of the ungodly, nor stands in the path of sinners, nor sits in the seat of the scornful, but his delight is in the law of the Lord, and in His law he meditates day and night. He shall be like a tree planted by the rivers of water, that brings forth its fruit in its season, whose leaf also shall not wither; and whatever he does shall prosper." Psalm 1:1-3

Date: ______________________________

Scripture: ______________________________

Insights and Personal Application:

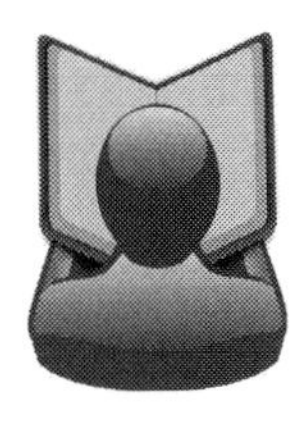

Meditation on the Word

"Blessed is the man who walks not in the counsel of the ungodly, nor stands in the path of sinners, nor sits in the seat of the scornful, but his delight is in the law of the Lord, and in His law he meditates day and night. He shall be like a tree planted by the rivers of water, that brings forth its fruit in its season, whose leaf also shall not wither; and whatever he does shall prosper." Psalm 1:1-3

Date: ______________________________

Scripture: ______________________________

____

____

____

____

____

Insights and Personal Application:

____

____

____

____

____

____

____

____

____

____

____

____

____

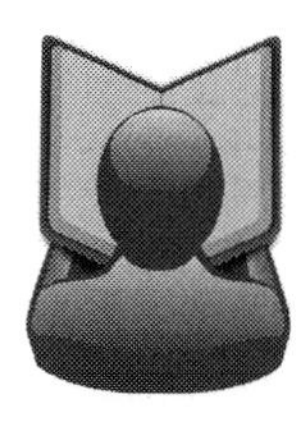

Meditation on the Word

"Blessed is the man who walks not in the counsel of the ungodly, nor stands in the path of sinners, nor sits in the seat of the scornful, but his delight is in the law of the Lord, and in His law he meditates day and night. He shall be like a tree planted by the rivers of water, that brings forth its fruit in its season, whose leaf also shall not wither; and whatever he does shall prosper." Psalm 1:1-3

Date: ______________________________

Scripture: ______________________________

____

____

____

____

____

Insights and Personal Application:

____

____

____

____

____

____

____

____

____

____

____

____

____

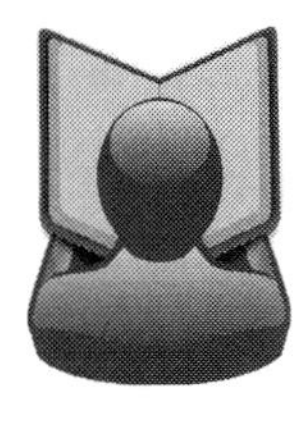

Meditation on the Word

"Blessed is the man who walks not in the counsel of the ungodly, nor stands in the path of sinners, nor sits in the seat of the scornful, but his delight is in the law of the Lord, and in His law he meditates day and night. He shall be like a tree planted by the rivers of water, that brings forth its fruit in its season, whose leaf also shall not wither; and whatever he does shall prosper." Psalm 1:1-3

Date: ______________________

Scripture: ______________________

____

____

____

____

____

Insights and Personal Application:

____

____

____

____

____

____

____

____

____

____

____

____

____

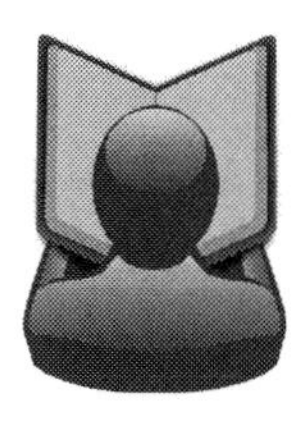

Meditation on the Word

"Blessed is the man who walks not in the counsel of the ungodly, nor stands in the path of sinners, nor sits in the seat of the scornful, but his delight is in the law of the Lord, and in His law he meditates day and night. He shall be like a tree planted by the rivers of water, that brings forth its fruit in its season, whose leaf also shall not wither; and whatever he does shall prosper." Psalm 1:1-3

Date: ______________________

Scripture: ______________________

Insights and Personal Application:

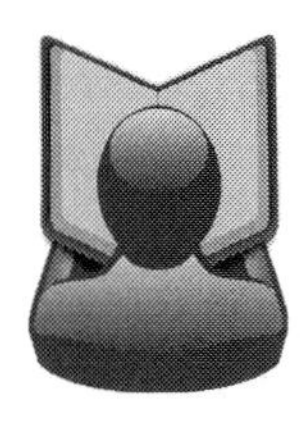

Meditation on the Word

"Blessed is the man who walks not in the counsel of the ungodly, nor stands in the path of sinners, nor sits in the seat of the scornful, but his delight is in the law of the Lord, and in His law he meditates day and night. He shall be like a tree planted by the rivers of water, that brings forth its fruit in its season, whose leaf also shall not wither; and whatever he does shall prosper." Psalm 1:1-3

Date: ______________________________

Scripture: ______________________________

Insights and Personal Application:

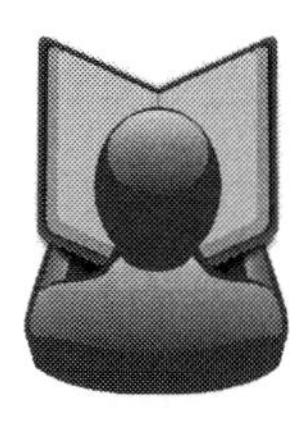

Meditation on the Word

"Blessed is the man who walks not in the counsel of the ungodly, nor stands in the path of sinners, nor sits in the seat of the scornful, but his delight is in the law of the Lord, and in His law he meditates day and night. He shall be like a tree planted by the rivers of water, that brings forth its fruit in its season, whose leaf also shall not wither; and whatever he does shall prosper." Psalm 1:1-3

Date: ______________________________

Scripture: ______________________________

____

____

____

____

____

Insights and Personal Application:

____

____

____

____

____

____

____

____

____

____

____

____

____

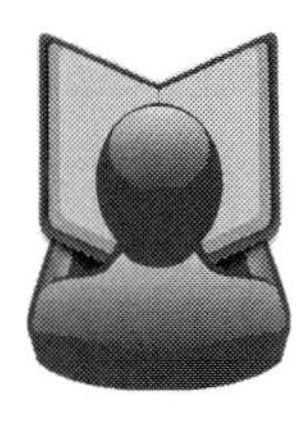

Meditation on the Word

"Blessed is the man who walks not in the counsel of the ungodly, nor stands in the path of sinners, nor sits in the seat of the scornful, but his delight is in the law of the Lord, and in His law he meditates day and night. He shall be like a tree planted by the rivers of water, that brings forth its fruit in its season, whose leaf also shall not wither; and whatever he does shall prosper." Psalm 1:1-3

Date: ____________________

Scripture: ____________________

Insights and Personal Application:

Meditation on the Word

"Blessed is the man who walks not in the counsel of the ungodly, nor stands in the path of sinners, nor sits in the seat of the scornful, but his delight is in the law of the Lord, and in His law he meditates day and night. He shall be like a tree planted by the rivers of water, that brings forth its fruit in its season, whose leaf also shall not wither; and whatever he does shall prosper." Psalm 1:1-3

Date: ______________________________

Scripture: ______________________________

____

____

____

____

____

Insights and Personal Application:

____

____

____

____

____

____

____

____

____

____

____

____

____

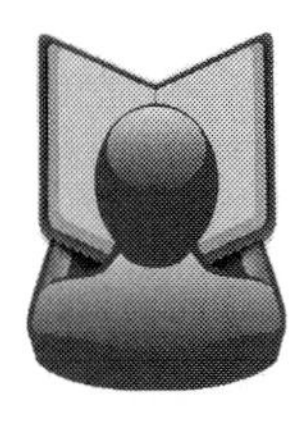

Meditation on the Word

"Blessed is the man who walks not in the counsel of the ungodly, nor stands in the path of sinners, nor sits in the seat of the scornful, but his delight is in the law of the Lord, and in His law he meditates day and night. He shall be like a tree planted by the rivers of water, that brings forth its fruit in its season, whose leaf also shall not wither; and whatever he does shall prosper." Psalm 1:1-3

Date: ______________________________

Scripture: ______________________________

____

____

____

____

____

Insights and Personal Application:

____

____

____

____

____

____

____

____

____

____

____

____

____

Meditation on the Word

"Blessed is the man who walks not in the counsel of the ungodly, nor stands in the path of sinners, nor sits in the seat of the scornful, but his delight is in the law of the Lord, and in His law he meditates day and night. He shall be like a tree planted by the rivers of water, that brings forth its fruit in its season, whose leaf also shall not wither; and whatever he does shall prosper." Psalm 1:1-3

Date: ______________________

Scripture: ______________________

Insights and Personal Application:

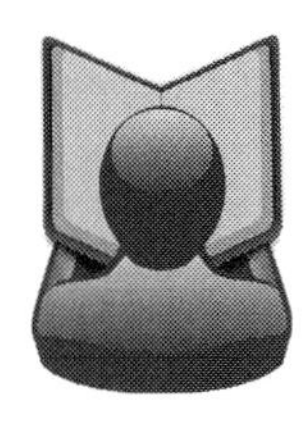

Meditation on the Word

"Blessed is the man who walks not in the counsel of the ungodly, nor stands in the path of sinners, nor sits in the seat of the scornful, but his delight is in the law of the Lord, and in His law he meditates day and night. He shall be like a tree planted by the rivers of water, that brings forth its fruit in its season, whose leaf also shall not wither; and whatever he does shall prosper." Psalm 1:1-3

Date: ____________________

Scripture: ______________________________________

____

____

____

____

____

Insights and Personal Application:

____

____

____

____

____

____

____

____

____

____

____

____

____

Meditation on the Word

"Blessed is the man who walks not in the counsel of the ungodly, nor stands in the path of sinners, nor sits in the seat of the scornful, but his delight is in the law of the Lord, and in His law he meditates day and night. He shall be like a tree planted by the rivers of water, that brings forth its fruit in its season, whose leaf also shall not wither; and whatever he does shall prosper." Psalm 1:1-3

Date: ____________________

Scripture: ____________________

Insights and Personal Application:

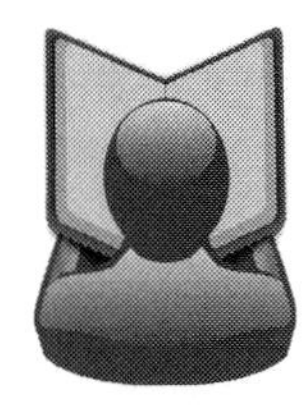

Meditation on the Word

"Blessed is the man who walks not in the counsel of the ungodly, nor stands in the path of sinners, nor sits in the seat of the scornful, but his delight is in the law of the Lord, and in His law he meditates day and night. He shall be like a tree planted by the rivers of water, that brings forth its fruit in its season, whose leaf also shall not wither; and whatever he does shall prosper." Psalm 1:1-3

Date: ____________________

Scripture: ____________________

Insights and Personal Application:

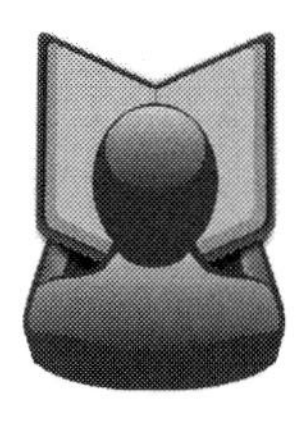

Meditation on the Word

"Blessed is the man who walks not in the counsel of the ungodly, nor stands in the path of sinners, nor sits in the seat of the scornful, but his delight is in the law of the Lord, and in His law he meditates day and night. He shall be like a tree planted by the rivers of water, that brings forth its fruit in its season, whose leaf also shall not wither; and whatever he does shall prosper." Psalm 1:1-3

Date: ______________________

Scripture: ______________________

Insights and Personal Application:

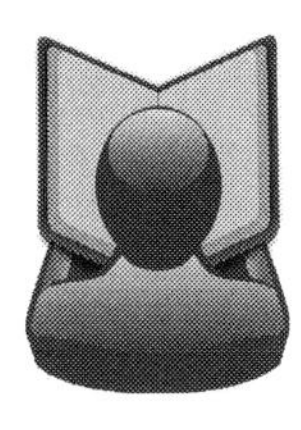

Meditation on the Word

"Blessed is the man who walks not in the counsel of the ungodly, nor stands in the path of sinners, nor sits in the seat of the scornful, but his delight is in the law of the Lord, and in His law he meditates day and night. He shall be like a tree planted by the rivers of water, that brings forth its fruit in its season, whose leaf also shall not wither; and whatever he does shall prosper." Psalm 1:1-3

Date: ______________________________

Scripture: ______________________________

Insights and Personal Application:

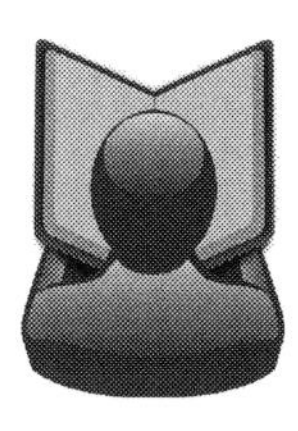

Meditation on the Word

"Blessed is the man who walks not in the counsel of the ungodly, nor stands in the path of sinners, nor sits in the seat of the scornful, but his delight is in the law of the Lord, and in His law he meditates day and night. He shall be like a tree planted by the rivers of water, that brings forth its fruit in its season, whose leaf also shall not wither; and whatever he does shall prosper." Psalm 1:1-3

Date: ______________________

Scripture: ______________________

Insights and Personal Application:

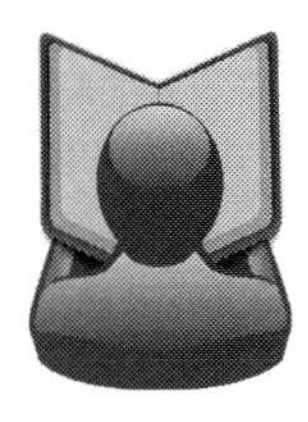

Meditation on the Word

"Blessed is the man who walks not in the counsel of the ungodly, nor stands in the path of sinners, nor sits in the seat of the scornful, but his delight is in the law of the Lord, and in His law he meditates day and night. He shall be like a tree planted by the rivers of water, that brings forth its fruit in its season, whose leaf also shall not wither; and whatever he does shall prosper." Psalm 1:1-3

Date: ______________________

Scripture: ______________________

Insights and Personal Application:

Meditation on the Word

"Blessed is the man who walks not in the counsel of the ungodly, nor stands in the path of sinners, nor sits in the seat of the scornful, but his delight is in the law of the Lord, and in His law he meditates day and night. He shall be like a tree planted by the rivers of water, that brings forth its fruit in its season, whose leaf also shall not wither; and whatever he does shall prosper." Psalm 1:1-3

Date: ______________________________

Scripture: ______________________________

____

____

____

____

____

Insights and Personal Application:

____

____

____

____

____

____

____

____

____

____

____

____

____

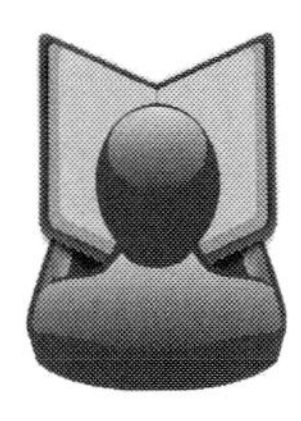

Meditation on the Word

"Blessed is the man who walks not in the counsel of the ungodly, nor stands in the path of sinners, nor sits in the seat of the scornful, but his delight is in the law of the Lord, and in His law he meditates day and night. He shall be like a tree planted by the rivers of water, that brings forth its fruit in its season, whose leaf also shall not wither; and whatever he does shall prosper." Psalm 1:1-3

Date: ______________________________

Scripture: ______________________________

Insights and Personal Application:

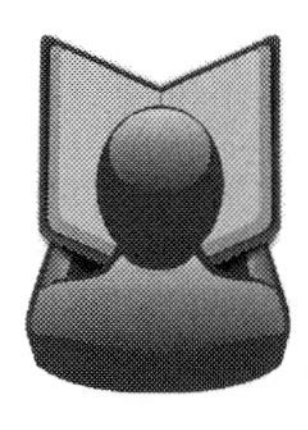

Meditation on the Word

"Blessed is the man who walks not in the counsel of the ungodly, nor stands in the path of sinners, nor sits in the seat of the scornful, but his delight is in the law of the Lord, and in His law he meditates day and night. He shall be like a tree planted by the rivers of water, that brings forth its fruit in its season, whose leaf also shall not wither; and whatever he does shall prosper." Psalm 1:1-3

Date: ______________________________

Scripture: ______________________________

____

____

____

____

____

Insights and Personal Application:

____

____

____

____

____

____

____

____

____

____

____

____

____

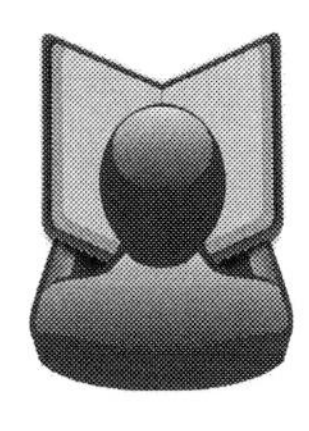

Meditation on the Word

"Blessed is the man who walks not in the counsel of the ungodly, nor stands in the path of sinners, nor sits in the seat of the scornful, but his delight is in the law of the Lord, and in His law he meditates day and night. He shall be like a tree planted by the rivers of water, that brings forth its fruit in its season, whose leaf also shall not wither; and whatever he does shall prosper." Psalm 1:1-3

Date: ______________________________

Scripture: ______________________________

____

____

____

____

____

Insights and Personal Application:

____

____

____

____

____

____

____

____

____

____

____

____

____

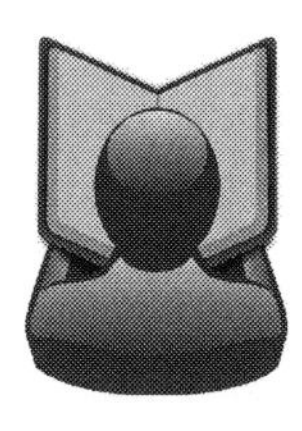

Meditation on the Word

"Blessed is the man who walks not in the counsel of the ungodly, nor stands in the path of sinners, nor sits in the seat of the scornful, but his delight is in the law of the Lord, and in His law he meditates day and night. He shall be like a tree planted by the rivers of water, that brings forth its fruit in its season, whose leaf also shall not wither; and whatever he does shall prosper." Psalm 1:1-3

Date: ______________________________

Scripture: ______________________________

____

____

____

____

____

Insights and Personal Application:

____

____

____

____

____

____

____

____

____

____

____

____

____

7

He Speaks to Me Daily Journal

He Speaks to Me Daily Journal

"My sheep hear my voice, and I know them, and they follow Me. And I will give them eternal life, and they shall never perish; neither shall anyone snatch them out of My hand." John 10: 27-28

Today, the Lord is saying: **Date:** ____________________

____

____

____

____

____

____

____

____

____

____

____

Today, the Lord is saying: **Date:** ____________________

____

____

____

____

____

____

____

____

____

____

____

He Speaks to Me Daily Journal

"My sheep hear my voice, and I know them, and they follow Me. And I will give them eternal life, and they shall never perish; neither shall anyone snatch them out of My hand." John 10: 27-28

Today, the Lord is saying: **Date:** ____________________

Today, the Lord is saying: **Date:** ____________________

He Speaks to Me Daily Journal

"My sheep hear my voice, and I know them, and they follow Me. And I will give them eternal life, and they shall never perish; neither shall anyone snatch them out of My hand." John 10: 27-28

Today, the Lord is saying: **Date:** ____________________

____

____

____

____

____

____

____

____

____

____

Today, the Lord is saying: **Date:** ____________________

____

____

____

____

____

____

____

____

____

____

____

He Speaks to Me Daily Journal

"My sheep hear my voice, and I know them, and they follow Me. And I will give them eternal life, and they shall never perish; neither shall anyone snatch them out of My hand." John 10: 27-28

Today, the Lord is saying: **Date:** ____________________

Today, the Lord is saying: **Date:** ____________________

He Speaks to Me Daily Journal

"My sheep hear my voice, and I know them, and they follow Me. And I will give them eternal life, and they shall never perish; neither shall anyone snatch them out of My hand." John 10: 27-28

Today, the Lord is saying: **Date:** ____________________

____

____

____

____

____

____

____

____

____

____

____

Today, the Lord is saying: **Date:** ____________________

____

____

____

____

____

____

____

____

____

____

____

He Speaks to Me Daily Journal

"My sheep hear my voice, and I know them, and they follow Me. And I will give them eternal life, and they shall never perish; neither shall anyone snatch them out of My hand." John 10: 27-28

Today, the Lord is saying: **Date:** ____________________

Today, the Lord is saying: **Date:** ____________________

He Speaks to Me Daily Journal

"My sheep hear my voice, and I know them, and they follow Me. And I will give them eternal life, and they shall never perish; neither shall anyone snatch them out of My hand." John 10: 27-28

Today, the Lord is saying: **Date:** ______________________

____

____

____

____

____

____

____

____

____

____

____

Today, the Lord is saying: **Date:** ______________________

____

____

____

____

____

____

____

____

____

____

____

He Speaks to Me Daily Journal

"My sheep hear my voice, and I know them, and they follow Me. And I will give them eternal life, and they shall never perish; neither shall anyone snatch them out of My hand." John 10: 27-28

Today, the Lord is saying: **Date:** ______________________

____
____
____
____
____
____
____
____
____
____

Today, the Lord is saying: **Date:** ______________________

____
____
____
____
____
____
____
____
____
____
____

He Speaks to Me Daily Journal

"My sheep hear my voice, and I know them, and they follow Me. And I will give them eternal life, and they shall never perish; neither shall anyone snatch them out of My hand." John 10: 27-28

Today, the Lord is saying: **Date:** ______________________

____

____

____

____

____

____

____

____

____

____

____

Today, the Lord is saying: **Date:** ______________________

____

____

____

____

____

____

____

____

____

____

____

He Speaks to Me Daily Journal

"My sheep hear my voice, and I know them, and they follow Me. And I will give them eternal life, and they shall never perish; neither shall anyone snatch them out of My hand." John 10: 27-28

Today, the Lord is saying: Date: ____________________

Today, the Lord is saying: Date: ____________________

He Speaks to Me Daily Journal

"My sheep hear my voice, and I know them, and they follow Me. And I will give them eternal life, and they shall never perish; neither shall anyone snatch them out of My hand." John 10: 27-28

Today, the Lord is saying: **Date:** ____________________

____
____
____
____
____
____
____
____
____
____
____

Today, the Lord is saying: **Date:** ____________________

____
____
____
____
____
____
____
____
____
____
____

He Speaks to Me Daily Journal

"My sheep hear my voice, and I know them, and they follow Me. And I will give them eternal life, and they shall never perish; neither shall anyone snatch them out of My hand." John 10: 27-28

Today, the Lord is saying: **Date:** ____________________

Today, the Lord is saying: **Date:** ____________________

He Speaks to Me Daily Journal

"My sheep hear my voice, and I know them, and they follow Me. And I will give them eternal life, and they shall never perish; neither shall anyone snatch them out of My hand." John 10: 27-28

Today, the Lord is saying: **Date:** ____________

____
____
____
____
____
____
____
____
____
____
____

Today, the Lord is saying: **Date:** ____________

____
____
____
____
____
____
____
____
____
____
____

He Speaks to Me Daily Journal

"My sheep hear my voice, and I know them, and they follow Me. And I will give them eternal life, and they shall never perish; neither shall anyone snatch them out of My hand." John 10: 27-28

Today, the Lord is saying: **Date:** ____________________

____

____

____

____

____

____

____

____

____

____

____

Today, the Lord is saying: **Date:** ____________________

____

____

____

____

____

____

____

____

____

____

____

He Speaks to Me Daily Journal

"My sheep hear my voice, and I know them, and they follow Me. And I will give them eternal life, and they shall never perish; neither shall anyone snatch them out of My hand." John 10: 27-28

Today, the Lord is saying: **Date:** ____________________

____

____

____

____

____

____

____

____

____

____

____

Today, the Lord is saying: **Date:** ____________________

____

____

____

____

____

____

____

____

____

____

____

He Speaks to Me Daily Journal

"My sheep hear my voice, and I know them, and they follow Me. And I will give them eternal life, and they shall never perish; neither shall anyone snatch them out of My hand." John 10: 27-28

Today, the Lord is saying: **Date:** ____________________

____
____
____
____
____
____
____
____
____
____
____

Today, the Lord is saying: **Date:** ____________________

____
____
____
____
____
____
____
____
____
____
____

He Speaks to Me Daily Journal

"My sheep hear my voice, and I know them, and they follow Me. And I will give them eternal life, and they shall never perish; neither shall anyone snatch them out of My hand." John 10: 27-28

Today, the Lord is saying: **Date:** ____________________

Today, the Lord is saying: **Date:** ____________________

He Speaks to Me Daily Journal

"My sheep hear my voice, and I know them, and they follow Me. And I will give them eternal life, and they shall never perish; neither shall anyone snatch them out of My hand." John 10: 27-28

Today, the Lord is saying: **Date:** ____________________

____
____
____
____
____
____
____
____
____
____
____

Today, the Lord is saying: **Date:** ____________________

____
____
____
____
____
____
____
____
____
____
____

He Speaks to Me Daily Journal

"My sheep hear my voice, and I know them, and they follow Me. And I will give them eternal life, and they shall never perish; neither shall anyone snatch them out of My hand." John 10: 27-28

Today, the Lord is saying: **Date:** ______________________

____

____

____

____

____

____

____

____

____

____

____

Today, the Lord is saying: **Date:** ______________________

____

____

____

____

____

____

____

____

____

____

____

He Speaks to Me Daily Journal

"My sheep hear my voice, and I know them, and they follow Me. And I will give them eternal life, and they shall never perish; neither shall anyone snatch them out of My hand." John 10: 27-28

Today, the Lord is saying: **Date:** ____________________

Today, the Lord is saying: **Date:** ____________________

He Speaks to Me Daily Journal

"My sheep hear my voice, and I know them, and they follow Me. And I will give them eternal life, and they shall never perish; neither shall anyone snatch them out of My hand." John 10: 27-28

Today, the Lord is saying: **Date:** ______________________

____

____

____

____

____

____

____

____

____

____

____

Today, the Lord is saying: **Date:** ______________________

____

____

____

____

____

____

____

____

____

____

____

He Speaks to Me Daily Journal

"My sheep hear my voice, and I know them, and they follow Me. And I will give them eternal life, and they shall never perish; neither shall anyone snatch them out of My hand." John 10: 27-28

Today, the Lord is saying: **Date:** ____________________

____

____

____

____

____

____

____

____

____

____

____

Today, the Lord is saying: **Date:** ____________________

____

____

____

____

____

____

____

____

____

____

____

He Speaks to Me Daily Journal

"My sheep hear my voice, and I know them, and they follow Me. And I will give them eternal life, and they shall never perish; neither shall anyone snatch them out of My hand." John 10: 27-28

Today, the Lord is saying: Date: ______________

Today, the Lord is saying: Date: ______________

He Speaks to Me
Daily Journal

"My sheep hear my voice, and I know them, and they follow Me. And I will give them eternal life, and they shall never perish; neither shall anyone snatch them out of My hand." John 10: 27-28

Today, the Lord is saying: **Date:** ______________________

Today, the Lord is saying: **Date:** ______________________

He Speaks to Me Daily Journal

"My sheep hear my voice, and I know them, and they follow Me. And I will give them eternal life, and they shall never perish; neither shall anyone snatch them out of My hand." John 10: 27-28

Today, the Lord is saying: **Date:** ____________________

___

___

___

___

___

___

___

___

___

___

Today, the Lord is saying: **Date:** ____________________

___

___

___

___

___

___

___

___

___

___

___

He Speaks to Me Daily Journal

"My sheep hear my voice, and I know them, and they follow Me. And I will give them eternal life, and they shall never perish; neither shall anyone snatch them out of My hand." John 10: 27-28

Today, the Lord is saying: **Date:** ____________________

____

____

____

____

____

____

____

____

____

____

Today, the Lord is saying: **Date:** ____________________

____

____

____

____

____

____

____

____

____

____

____

He Speaks to Me Daily Journal

"My sheep hear my voice, and I know them, and they follow Me. And I will give them eternal life, and they shall never perish; neither shall anyone snatch them out of My hand." John 10: 27-28

Today, the Lord is saying: Date: ____________________

____

____

____

____

____

____

____

____

____

____

____

Today, the Lord is saying: Date: ____________________

____

____

____

____

____

____

____

____

____

____

____

He Speaks to Me Daily Journal

"My sheep hear my voice, and I know them, and they follow Me. And I will give them eternal life, and they shall never perish; neither shall anyone snatch them out of My hand." John 10: 27-28

Today, the Lord is saying: **Date:** ______________________

____

____

____

____

____

____

____

____

____

____

____

Today, the Lord is saying: **Date:** ______________________

____

____

____

____

____

____

____

____

____

____

____

He Speaks to Me Daily Journal

"My sheep hear my voice, and I know them, and they follow Me. And I will give them eternal life, and they shall never perish; neither shall anyone snatch them out of My hand." John 10: 27-28

Today, the Lord is saying: **Date:** ______________________

____

____

____

____

____

____

____

____

____

____

____

Today, the Lord is saying: **Date:** ______________________

____

____

____

____

____

____

____

____

____

____

____

He Speaks to Me
Daily Journal

"My sheep hear my voice, and I know them, and they follow Me. And I will give them eternal life, and they shall never perish; neither shall anyone snatch them out of My hand." John 10: 27-28

Today, the Lord is saying: **Date:** ____________________

____

____

____

____

____

____

____

____

____

____

____

Today, the Lord is saying: **Date:** ____________________

____

____

____

____

____

____

____

____

____

____

____

He Speaks to Me Daily Journal

"My sheep hear my voice, and I know them, and they follow Me. And I will give them eternal life, and they shall never perish; neither shall anyone snatch them out of My hand." John 10: 27-28

Today, the Lord is saying: **Date:** ____________________

____

____

____

____

____

____

____

____

____

____

____

Today, the Lord is saying: **Date:** ____________________

____

____

____

____

____

____

____

____

____

____

____

He Speaks to Me Daily Journal

"My sheep hear my voice, and I know them, and they follow Me. And I will give them eternal life, and they shall never perish; neither shall anyone snatch them out of My hand." John 10: 27-28

Today, the Lord is saying: **Date:** ____________________

Today, the Lord is saying: **Date:** ____________________

He Speaks to Me Daily Journal

"My sheep hear my voice, and I know them, and they follow Me. And I will give them eternal life, and they shall never perish; neither shall anyone snatch them out of My hand." John 10: 27-28

Today, the Lord is saying: **Date:** ____________________

Today, the Lord is saying: **Date:** ____________________

He Speaks to Me Daily Journal

"My sheep hear my voice, and I know them, and they follow Me. And I will give them eternal life, and they shall never perish; neither shall anyone snatch them out of My hand." John 10: 27-28

Today, the Lord is saying: **Date:** ______________________

____

____

____

____

____

____

____

____

____

____

____

Today, the Lord is saying: **Date:** ______________________

____

____

____

____

____

____

____

____

____

____

____

He Speaks to Me Daily Journal

"My sheep hear my voice, and I know them, and they follow Me. And I will give them eternal life, and they shall never perish; neither shall anyone snatch them out of My hand." John 10: 27-28

Today, the Lord is saying: Date: ____________________

____
____
____
____
____
____
____
____
____
____

Today, the Lord is saying: Date: ____________________

____
____
____
____
____
____
____
____
____
____
____

He Speaks to Me Daily Journal

"My sheep hear my voice, and I know them, and they follow Me. And I will give them eternal life, and they shall never perish; neither shall anyone snatch them out of My hand." John 10: 27-28

Today, the Lord is saying: **Date:** ____________________

____

____

____

____

____

____

____

____

____

____

Today, the Lord is saying: **Date:** ____________________

____

____

____

____

____

____

____

____

____

____

He Speaks to Me Daily Journal

"My sheep hear my voice, and I know them, and they follow Me. And I will give them eternal life, and they shall never perish; neither shall anyone snatch them out of My hand." John 10: 27-28

Today, the Lord is saying: **Date:** ____________________

Today, the Lord is saying: **Date:** ____________________

He Speaks to Me Daily Journal

"My sheep hear my voice, and I know them, and they follow Me. And I will give them eternal life, and they shall never perish; neither shall anyone snatch them out of My hand." John 10: 27-28

Today, the Lord is saying: **Date:** ____________________

____

____

____

____

____

____

____

____

____

____

____

Today, the Lord is saying: **Date:** ____________________

____

____

____

____

____

____

____

____

____

____

____

He Speaks to Me Daily Journal

"My sheep hear my voice, and I know them, and they follow Me. And I will give them eternal life, and they shall never perish; neither shall anyone snatch them out of My hand." John 10: 27-28

Today, the Lord is saying: **Date:** ____________________

____

____

____

____

____

____

____

____

____

____

____

Today, the Lord is saying: **Date:** ____________________

____

____

____

____

____

____

____

____

____

____

____

He Speaks to Me Daily Journal

"My sheep hear my voice, and I know them, and they follow Me. And I will give them eternal life, and they shall never perish; neither shall anyone snatch them out of My hand." John 10: 27-28

Today, the Lord is saying: **Date:** ____________________

Today, the Lord is saying: **Date:** ____________________

He Speaks to Me Daily Journal

"My sheep hear my voice, and I know them, and they follow Me. And I will give them eternal life, and they shall never perish; neither shall anyone snatch them out of My hand." John 10: 27-28

Today, the Lord is saying: **Date:** ____________________

Today, the Lord is saying: **Date:** ____________________

He Speaks to Me Daily Journal

"My sheep hear my voice, and I know them, and they follow Me. And I will give them eternal life, and they shall never perish; neither shall anyone snatch them out of My hand." John 10: 27-28

Today, the Lord is saying: **Date:** ____________________

____

____

____

____

____

____

____

____

____

____

____

Today, the Lord is saying: **Date:** ____________________

____

____

____

____

____

____

____

____

____

____

____

He Speaks to Me Daily Journal

"My sheep hear my voice, and I know them, and they follow Me. And I will give them eternal life, and they shall never perish; neither shall anyone snatch them out of My hand." John 10: 27-28

Today, the Lord is saying: **Date:** ____________________

____

____

____

____

____

____

____

____

____

____

____

Today, the Lord is saying: **Date:** ____________________

____

____

____

____

____

____

____

____

____

____

____

He Speaks to Me Daily Journal

"My sheep hear my voice, and I know them, and they follow Me. And I will give them eternal life, and they shall never perish; neither shall anyone snatch them out of My hand." John 10: 27-28

Today, the Lord is saying: **Date:** ____________________

____

____

____

____

____

____

____

____

____

____

____

Today, the Lord is saying: **Date:** ____________________

____

____

____

____

____

____

____

____

____

____

____

He Speaks to Me Daily Journal

"My sheep hear my voice, and I know them, and they follow Me. And I will give them eternal life, and they shall never perish; neither shall anyone snatch them out of My hand." John 10: 27-28

Today, the Lord is saying: **Date:** ____________________

____
____
____
____
____
____
____
____
____
____
____

Today, the Lord is saying: **Date:** ____________________

____
____
____
____
____
____
____
____
____
____
____

He Speaks to Me Daily Journal

"My sheep hear my voice, and I know them, and they follow Me. And I will give them eternal life, and they shall never perish; neither shall anyone snatch them out of My hand." John 10: 27-28

Today, the Lord is saying: **Date:** ______________________

____

____

____

____

____

____

____

____

____

____

____

Today, the Lord is saying: **Date:** ______________________

____

____

____

____

____

____

____

____

____

____

____

He Speaks to Me Daily Journal

"My sheep hear my voice, and I know them, and they follow Me. And I will give them eternal life, and they shall never perish; neither shall anyone snatch them out of My hand." John 10: 27-28

Today, the Lord is saying: **Date:** ______________________

____
____
____
____
____
____
____
____
____
____
____

Today, the Lord is saying: **Date:** ______________________

____
____
____
____
____
____
____
____
____
____
____

8

Prophetic Words

Prophetic Words

"But he who prophesies speaks edification and exhortation and comfort to men." 1 Corinthians 14:3

Date	Word/Request	Date Answered

Prophetic Words

"But he who prophesies speaks edification and exhortation and comfort to men." 1 Corinthians 14:3

Date	Word/Request	Date Answered

Prophetic Words

"But he who prophesies speaks edification and exhortation and comfort to men." 1 Corinthians 14:3

Date	Word/Request	Date Answered

Prophetic Words

"But he who prophesies speaks edification and exhortation and comfort to men." 1 Corinthians 14:3

Date	Word/Request	Date Answered

Prophetic Words

"But he who prophesies speaks edification and exhortation and comfort to men." 1 Corinthians 14:3

Date	Word/Request	Date Answered

Prophetic Words

"But he who prophesies speaks edification and exhortation and comfort to men." 1 Corinthians 14:3

Date	Word/Request	Date Answered

Prophetic Words

"But he who prophesies speaks edification and exhortation and comfort to men." 1 Corinthians 14:3

Date	Word/Request	Date Answered

9

Memory Verses

Why Pray?

10 Commandments

Memory Verses

Trust in the Lord with all your heart, and lean not unto your own understanding, in all your ways acknowledge Him, and He shall direct your paths.

Proverbs 3:5-6

...God has not given us a spirit of fear, but of power and of love and of a sound mind.

2 Timothy 1:7

He who is in you is greater than he who is in the world.

1 John 4:4

I, even I, am He who comforts you. Who are you that you should be afraid of a man who will die?

Isaiah 51:12

If I say my foot slips, Your mercy, O Lord, will hold me up. In the multitude of my anxieties within me, Your comfort delights my soul.

Psalm 94:18-19

If we confess our sins, He is faithful and just to forgive us our sins and to cleanse us from all unrighteousness.

1 John 1:9

But God demonstrates His own love toward us, in that while we were still sinners, Christ died for us.

Romans 5:8

Create in me a clean heart, O God, and renew a steadfast spirit within me. Do not cast me away from Your presence, and do not take Your Holy Spirit from me. Restore to me the joy of Your salvation, and uphold me with your generous Spirit. Then I will teach transgressors Your ways, and sinners shall be converted to You.

Psalm 51:10-13

For I know the thoughts that I think toward you, says the Lord, thoughts of peace and not of evil, to give you a future and a hope. Then you will call upon Me and go and pray to Me, and I will listen to you. And you will seek Me and find Me when you search for Me with all your heart.

Jeremiah 29:11-13

I will not leave you orphans; I will come to you.

John 14:18

We love Him because He first loved us.

1 John 4:19

He who has begun a good work in you will complete it until the day of Jesus Christ.

Phillipians 1:6

I will not leave you nor forsake you.

Joshua 1:5

How can a young man cleanse his way? By taking heed according to Your word.

Psalm 119:9

Turn away my eyes from looking at worthless things, and revive me in Your way.

Psalm 119:37

Why Pray?

Therefore I say to you, whatever things you ask when you pray, believe that you receive them, and you will have them.

Mark 11:24

But without faith it is impossible to please Him, for he who comes to God must believe that He is, and that He is a rewarder of those who diligently seek Him.

Hebrews 11:6

Confess your trespasses to one another, and pray for one another, that you may be healed. The effective, fervent prayer of a righteous man avails much.

James 5:16

Elijah was a man with a nature like ours, and he prayed earnestly that it would not rain; and it did not rain on the land for three years and six months. And he prayed again, and the heaven gave rain, and the earth produced its fruit.

James 5:17-18

Be anxious for nothing but in everything by prayer and supplication, with thanksgiving, let your requests be made known to God; and the peace of God which surpasses all understanding, will guard your hearts and minds through Christ Jesus.

Phillipians 4:6-7

If I regard iniquity in my heart, the Lord will not hear. But certainly God has heard me; He has attended to the voice of my prayer.

Psalm 66:18-19

The Lord is near to all who call upon Him, to all who call upon Him in truth.

Psalm 145:18

Then He spoke a parable to them, that men always ought to pray and not lose heart.

Luke 18:1

And all things, whatever you ask in prayer, believing, you will receive.

Matthew 21:22

But we will give ourselves continually to prayer and to the ministry of the word.

Acts 6:4

Continue earnestly in prayer, being vigilant in it with thanksgiving; meanwhile praying also for us, that God would open to us a door for the word, to speak the mystery of Christ.

Acts 4:2-3

Praying always with all prayer and supplication in the Spirit, being watchful to this end with all perseverance and supplication for all the saints.

Ephesians 6:18

Watch therefore, and pray always that you may be counted worthy to escape all these things that will come to pass, and to stand before the Son of Man.

Luke 21:36

But the prayer of the upright is His delight.

Proverbs 15:8

Father, I thank You that You have heard Me. And I know that You always hear Me.

John 11:41-42

The Ten Commandments

Memorize the Ten Commandments from Exodus, chapter 20, of the Holy Bible (NKJV). (They are also repeated in Deuteronomy, chapter 5).

I **"I am the Lord your God...you shall have no other gods before Me." Exodus 20:2,3** There is only One, True God. Trust Him only.

II **"You shall not make for yourself any carved image, or any likeness of anything that is in heaven above, or that is in the earth beneath, or that is in the water under the earth; you shall not bow down to them nor serve them." Exodus 20:4,5** Submit to and worship only the One, True God, not an image or likeness of any false god, idol, famous person, or even yourself.

III **"You shall not take the name of the Lord your God in vain, for the Lord will not hold him guiltless who takes His name in vain." Exodus 20:7** Regard God's name as holy and use it in ways that honor Him.

IV **"Remember the Sabbath day, to keep it holy." Exodus 20:8** Rest on the Sabbath day, in obedience and honor to God, who made it holy. Consider His goodness, mercies, promises, and love for you.

V **"Honor your father and your mother." Exodus 20:12** Respect and obey your parents.

VI **"You shall not murder." Exodus 20:13** Respect human life.

VII **"You shall not commit adultery." Exodus 20:14** Be faithful to your lawful spouse.

VIII **"You shall not steal." Exodus 20:15** Do not take another's belongings.

IX **"You shall not bear false witness against your neighbor." Exodus 20:16** Don't lie about other people.

X **"You shall not covet your neighbor's house...wife...nor anything that is your neighbor's." Exodus 20:17** Be satisfied with what you have—your house, your spouse, your property.

About the Author

Rosemary (R.K.) McWilliams grew up in northern Minnesota, where she became a born again Christian during the 1970s Jesus Movement. She moved to Texas, where she worked as a Respiratory Therapist/Pulmonary Function Technologist. There, she obtained a B.A.S. degree, with honors, from Wayland Baptist University.

Rosemary and her husband, Pastor Mark McWilliams, minister the Gospel of Jesus Christ in beautiful East Texas. Rosemary is retired from the medical field, but continues to write, as the Lord leads.

As a child, Rosemary was drawn to kneel at her bedside to pray before bedtime. As her prayer life grew, her relationship with the Lord grew and soon she desired to share what she learned with others. She learned that:

Prayer changes hearts
Prayer changes lives

This Intercessory Prayer Journal is the same journal she and her husband use every day, as they seek the Lord together. She knows that God is calling people to pray in these times and this book is a valuable tool to aid those who will pray.

Books by R.K. McWilliams

Enter My Rest
Enter My Rest Journal
Intercessory Prayer Journal
Chemical Chaos, Book 1 of the Blood Moon Series
Blood Moon Terrorists, Book 2 of the Blood Moon Series
Airtight Pulmonary Function Tests
Airtight Pulmonary Function Tests Workbook

All books can be found in print on Amazon.com
Amazon Author Page: amazon.com/author/rkmcwilliams
For special pricing on larger quantities, please order directly by writing to:
rkmcwilliamsbooks@gmail.com
rkmcwilliams.blogspot.com

NOTES

Made in the USA
Monee, IL
09 November 2021

81216690R00101